Developing Citizenship

ACTIVITIES FOR PERSONAL, SOCIAL ~~ATION~~

year

R

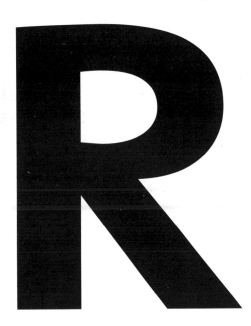

Christine Moorcroft

A & C BLACK

Contents

Published 2005 by A & C Black Publishers Limited
37 Soho Square, London W1D 3QZ
www.acblack.com

ISBN–10: 0-7136-7116-5
ISBN–13: 978-0-7136-7116-2

Copyright text © Christine Moorcroft, 2005
Copyright illustrations © Gaynor Berry, 2005
Copyright cover illustration © Graham Smith,
    The Bright Agency, 2005

Editor: Jane Klima
Design: Susan McIntyre

The author and publishers would like to thank Catherine Yemm
and Don Rowe for their assistance in producing this book.

A CIP catalogue record for this book is available from the British Library.

Printed in Great Britain by St Edmundsbury Press,
Bury St Edmunds, Suffolk.

A & C Black uses paper produced with elemental chlorine-free pulp, harvested from managed sustainable forests.

Developing Citizenship is a series of seven photocopiable activity books for citizenship lessons (including Personal, Social and Health Education and, in the foundation stage, *Personal, social and emotional development*). Each book provides a range of activities to help teachers to prepare children to play an active role as citizens, including:

- developing confidence and responsibility and making the most of their abilities;
- developing a healthy, safe lifestyle;
- developing good relationships and respecting differences between people;
- helping children to think for themselves, to express their own thoughts and opinions confidently, and to learn to listen to others' points of view;
- helping children to become full members of the groups they belong to, knowing they have rights but also becoming increasingly aware of their responsibilities.

The activities in **Year R** are based on *Curriculum guidance for the foundation stage: Personal, social and emotional development* and support children's development in the following areas:

- respecting themselves and others;
- valuing their culture and the cultures of others;
- relationships;
- the importance of friendships;
- positive attitudes towards learning;
- solving problems.

The activities are linked with other areas of the curriculum where appropriate and draw on the QCA schemes of work. Teachers are encouraged to introduce them in a stimulating environment that provides facilities for the children to explore and to develop a sense of responsibility: for example, equipment they can use for a specific purpose and then put away, tidy up or leave as they found it, such as magnets or magnifying glasses (and interesting objects to try to pick up or look at).

Each activity sheet features a **Teachers' note** at the foot of the page, which can be masked before photocopying if desired. Expanded teaching notes are provided in **Notes on the activities** on pages 5–11. Most of the activity sheets end with a challenge (**Now try this!**) which reinforces and extends the children's learning and provides the teacher with an opportunity for assessment. These extension activities might be appropriate for only a few children; it is not expected that the whole class should complete them. On some pages there is space for the children to complete these activities, but others will require a notebook or a separate sheet of paper.

Beyond the classroom

The series takes into account that unplanned experiences which the children have at school and in other places can contribute to the development of concepts and attitudes concerning citizenship. To help teachers to link children's learning through taught activities with their learning at other times, the teachers' notes make suggestions wherever possible for promoting the development of citizenship outside lessons.

Organisation

The activities require very few resources beyond pencils, scissors, card and other general classroom items. Any other materials you will need are specified in the **Notes on the activities** (for example, computers, information books and leaflets, pictures and story books).

Reading

Most children will be able to carry out the activities independently. It is not expected that they should be able to read all the instructions on the sheets, but that someone will read them to or with them. Children gradually become accustomed to seeing instructions, and learn their purpose long before they can read them for themselves.

Vocabulary

Key vocabulary to be introduced is provided in the **Notes on the activities**, to contribute to the children's skills in *Communication, language and literacy*.

Health and safety

Developing Citizenship provides advice on how to make lessons safe and how to encourage children to take responsibility for their own safety. Specific health and safety notes are included in the **Notes on the activities** where appropriate. Advice on implementing safe policy and practice for use of the Internet in schools can be found on the British Educational Communications and Technology Agency's website: www.becta.org.uk.

Useful websites

Citizenship education curriculum: www.dfes.gov.uk/citizenship (summarises the citizenship curriculum, offers free resources and links to the QCA schemes of work)

Institute for Citizenship: www.citizen.org.uk/education (ideas for classroom activities; links to websites offering useful information)

Schoolzone: www.schoolzone.co.uk (resources for teaching citizenship)

Eduwight (Isle of Wight Council's website for children's services): http://eduwight.iow.gov.uk/curriculum/vocational/citizenship/ (resources for teaching citizenship, including lesson plans)

PSHE and citizenship links: www.jamesbancrofteducation.net/pshe (online resources, including assembly ideas, for various citizenship topics, such as bullying; links to children's websites, including Childline and Kidscape)

Kelly Bear (a U.S. website featuring a positive role model for children aged 3–9): http://www.kellybear.com/TeacherArticles/TeacherTip27.html (20 ideas for teaching citizenship, including lesson plans)

The notes in this section expand upon those provided at the foot of each activity sheet. They give ideas for making the most of the sheet, including suggestions for a whole-class introduction or discussion, or for follow-up work using an adapted version of the page.

The notes also suggest links which can be made with other areas of the curriculum and ways of developing citizenship through everyday experiences: for example, involving the children in the planning of school events, discussing any problems the school faces and their possible solutions and involving the children in planning for changes at the school. An example faced by one school was the amalgamation with a neighbouring school. The teachers asked the children to think of ways of welcoming the newcomers and helping them to settle in.

To help teachers to select appropriate learning experiences for their pupils, the activities are grouped into sections within each book, but the pages need not be presented in the order in which they appear unless stated otherwise. Ideas for differentiation are suggested in the extension activities and in the notes below.

Where appropriate, stories, songs, rhymes, jingles and poems are suggested for introducing the activities or rounding them off.

Myself and people around me

These activities focus on the children's self-awareness and self-esteem and on the relationships they form with other children and with adults. In addition to the focus on *Personal, social and emotional development*, there are links with *Knowledge and understanding of the world* and *Communication, language and literacy* (especially where stories are the starting points). The game boards provide opportunities for making links with *Mathematical development*.

We are good at this (page 12) develops the children's sense of self and encourages them to value their strengths. You could introduce this activity by reading *Elmer* by David McKee (Andersen). Discuss what Elmer was good at doing (cheering

up the other elephants) and what was special about him. Why did the other elephants miss him when he left the herd? How did they recognise him after he had made himself grey like the others? Ask the children to think of things they and others in the class are good at. What do they miss when one of them is absent? Emphasise that people have different strengths and can be good at more than one thing. If possible, use an electronic version of the story with which the children can interact. Higher-attaining children might be able to describe what it means to be good at something: for example, good writing might be in a straight line with the tall letters all the same height. Being good at football might be scoring a lot of goals or passing the ball well to others in the team. The children could create different characters online at

www.bgfl.org/bgfl/custom/resources_ftp/client_ftp/ks1/english/characters/index.htm and then say or write what each character is good at.

> **Vocabulary:** *different, good, same, special, strength.*

Looking after Tom and **Stars** (pages 13–14) encourage the children to talk freely about their main carer and other important people in their lives. The

activities could be introduced through the story *Bye Bye Baby* by Janet and Allan Ahlberg (Mammoth), about a baby who looks after himself because he has no parents and goes looking for someone to be his mother. Ask the children how they feel about the baby who has no mother. He can look after himself very well – so why does he want a mother? Who else can look after children apart from their mother? Draw out that there are different kinds of families. *Catherine and Laurence Anholt's Big Book of Families* (Walker Books) is a good starting point for focusing on the many variations among families: the children will be able to identify with a family group similar to their own. *What's That Noise?* by Francesca Simon and David Melling (Hodder) is about Harry who is staying away from home for the first time and hears noises at night but is comforted by his grandfather. Lower-attaining children might need help in the form of questions: *Who is special at home?*, *What does he or she do that you like?*

> **Vocabulary:** *auntie, brother, care, dad, family, father, grandfather, grandmother, look after, love, mother, mum, sister, special, supervisor, teacher, uncle.*

Where I belong (page 15) encourages the children to talk freely about home and to develop their sense of self as a member of different communities. Ask them about their homes. What makes them special and different from other places? Draw out that a home is not just the place where we live; it includes the people who live there. What other places do they belong to and which people do they meet there? These might include their grandparents' home, a swimming club, their church, mosque or synagogue, their town or village, a local choir, Rainbows or Beavers. The children could also read the book *A House is a House for Me* by Mary Ann Hoberman (Picture Puffins); encourage them to compare the different homes in the book. Higher-attaining children might be able to identify any similar activities which they do in different places or explain why they do some things in one place and others in another place; point out that some activities are appropriate in one place but not in another. *Bob the Builder* activities for the foundation stage, linked to the British Educational Communications and Technology Agency (Becta) website, could be used for designing a house: http://hitentertainment.com/bobthebuilder/uk/bentley.html. These allow the children to choose the shape of a house, then a roof, then windows and a door and then to paint and print it. You could relate this activity to work in *Knowledge and understanding of the world* (Comment and ask questions about where they live).

> **Vocabulary:** *Beavers, belong, choir, church, club, family, home, house, member, mosque, Rainbows, school, synagogue, town, village.*

Is it time? (page 16) is about responding to significant experiences. It encourages the children to think of celebrations that have been meaningful, such as birthdays and religious and community celebrations. Useful stories include *Happy Birthday, Sam* by Pat Hutchins (Picture Puffins) and *Kipper's Birthday* by Mick Inkpen (Hodder). The activity focuses on the feelings generated by preparing for a celebration: excitement and impatience. You could also discuss how the children feel during the celebration and when it is all over. What memories do they have afterwards? Ask them to name mementoes that people often keep to remind them of their feelings on a special occasion: for example, photographs, videos, certificates, presents and cards. The children could also mark significant dates on a class calendar. This activity could link with *Knowledge and understanding of the world* (Find out about past and present events in their own lives and in those of their families and other people they know). The focus on time also provides opportunities to develop numeracy skills. Higher-attaining children might be able to draw and write their own story about a big occasion to which they looked forward. Show the children videos or DVDs of celebrations from different cultures and ask them how they can tell that people are celebrating.

> **Vocabulary:** *celebrate, excited, happy, impatient, party, share, time, together.*

My big day (page 17) is about responding to significant experiences; it encourages the children to think of special events they have taken part in or watched, such as sporting events, religious celebrations, outings, holidays, being given important items, and so on. The activity could be introduced through photographs of the children taking part in or watching these events: ask them to describe what they are doing in the photographs and how they felt at the time. You could also show them a video of an important event, e.g. a football team scoring a goal or an Olympic team winning a medal. Draw out the feeling of taking part along with other people and of sharing an experience. This activity could complement work in *Knowledge and understanding of the world* (Find out about past and present events in their own lives and in those of their families and other people they know).

> **Vocabulary:** *celebrate, day, event, important, occasion, people, share, special, time.*

What I like (page 18) encourages the children to express their feelings in appropriate ways. It also develops their ability to take turns in a conversation. They could first talk to a partner about something they like. Model this with another adult; ask the person questions about what he or she likes and demonstrate how to take turns in a conversation. Afterwards establish that while one person was talking the other listened and then asked questions to find out more. Ask the children what they found out by listening and asking questions. Some children could use the words on the page to help them to write sentences which begin *I like.*

> **Vocabulary:** *comfortable, dislike, exciting, frightening, fun, like, nice, pleasant, sweet, tasty, warm.*

Making friends (page 19) is about relating to others and making attachments to other members of the group. You could begin with a story about how not to behave towards others, such as *The Bad-Tempered Ladybird* by Eric Carle (Picture Puffins). Discuss what the bad-tempered ladybird did wrong and what the friendly ladybird did right. Which was the happier ladybird? *Little Bean's Friend* by John Wallace (Collins Picture Lions) explores the feeling of hesitation experienced by many children as they try to make friends. If Little Bean wanted to make friends with Paul, why didn't she want to go and talk to him at first? Who helped her? Encourage the children to imagine going into a playground where they do not know any of the children. What could they do to make friends? Discuss what might stop them going to talk to children they do not know: for example, fear that the children will not be friendly towards them. Ask them to think about how Eva feels at first and how she feels at the end of the story. Why is she feeling differently? Why is it nice to make friends? This could be explored further through the story *Do You Want to Be My Friend?* by Eric Carle (Picture Puffins). The children could enact these situations or write stories about them; encourage them to think of ways of making a newcomer feel welcome.

Health and safety: Ensure that the children know that they should not make friends with people their parents or carers do not know about.

> **Vocabulary:** *friend, friendly, help, kind, newcomer, share.*

Sam's pals (page 20) is about relating to others and making attachments to other members of the group. It explores the pleasure of having friends through focusing on activities which friends share. Lower-attaining children might need help in the form  of questions and hints: for example, *Who likes to watch TV with Sam? What shall we call his friends? Who can Sam play ball with? Think of a friend for him.*

> **Vocabulary:** *chat, friend, help, laugh, play, share, take turns, talk, together, work.*

Tell me why (page 21) is about developing flexibility and adapting to situations. It encourages the children to think about times when they have had to do things they did not want to do and to consider why the people who look after them sometimes insist that they do certain things. You could introduce this through reading some of the *Little Princess* stories by Tony Ross (Collins); *I Want My Dinner* is particularly suitable. Discuss what the little princess learned during this story and what she taught the monster. Higher-attaining children might be able to tell or write a longer story about what happened to a little boy or girl who wouldn't do as he or she was told – and about the consequences.

> **Vocabulary:** *obey, reason, rule, why.*

Right and wrong

The activities in this section help the children to develop an understanding of what is right and what is wrong, and why, and to consider the consequences of their words and actions for themselves and others. The activities also build on the children's ability to form relationships with others.

A time and a place (page 22) is about developing an awareness of boundaries and expectations. It focuses on the different types of behaviour that are appropriate in different places: for example, where it is appropriate and where it is not appropriate to run, shout, throw a ball or ride a bike, and why. You  could begin by asking silly questions such as *Is it all right to play football in your bedroom? Should you skateboard in the living room?* You could also provide pictures from magazines, brochures and colouring books that show children engaged in activities such as football, using computer games, squirting water or drawing. Ask them to name some places where these activities could take place. After the children have completed the sheet, you could focus on the word 'shout'. Have the children put a cross in this box? Can they think if it ever might be right to shout in the classroom? (For example, if there were a fire or to warn someone of danger.)

> **Vocabulary:** *allowed, all right, place, right, rule, rules, time, wrong.*

A helping hand (page 23) develops the children's consideration for others around them; it also links with work on developing a sense of responsibility for their own actions and towards the communities to which they belong and their concern for the environment. It is useful to discuss why the children should help at home. They might do so at present because they are rewarded or because they are told that they are 'good'. Explore with the children why it is seen as 'good' to help. How might it make other people feel? Draw out that helping is one of the many things we should do because they are right. The children could say how they feel when someone helps them.

> **Vocabulary:** *feelings, good, help, kind, unkind.*

A friend in need (page 24) focuses on showing care and concern for others. Encourage the children to imagine how they would feel in the situations in the pictures. What would help them to feel better? What kind of help would be useful? You could ask the children to think about questions like: Why should we help our friends? Should we help people who are not our friends? The children could make a classroom display of the ways in which they help one another, and the adults and children help one another, at school.

> **Vocabulary:** *comfort, friendly, happy, hurt, lonely, sad, unhappy.*

Pet care (page 25) helps to develop care and concern for living things and reinforces what the children learn through caring for animals at home and in the classroom. In order to be able to care for animals,  children need to know about their needs. This can be linked with work in *Knowledge and understanding of the world* (science) and possibly a class 'pet shop' or 'vet's surgery'. You could provide leaflets on animal care from veterinary surgeries and organisations such as the RSPCA and PDSA and read the important points with the children. They could also use web-based activities on animal homes designed for the foundation stage and linked to the Becta website:

www.bgfl.org/bgfl/custom/resources_ftp/client_ftp/ey/science/animal_h/index.htm. The children look at pictures of animals and click on their homes. They are told if they are right or wrong, and so on. See also the BBC's Little Animals website: http://www.bbc.co.uk/schools/laac/about.shtml.

> **Vocabulary:** *clean, drink, eat, food, healthy, look after, responsible, water.*

In **Spick and span** and **What a mess!** (pages 26–27) the focus is on caring for the children's immediate environment. The activities can draw on everyday classroom activities after which the children are expected to tidy up. Ask them what would happen if no one bothered to tidy up or clean up spills or if lids  were left off containers, and so on. Would they enjoy being in the classroom if it were like that? Stress that the classroom is *their* place. The children could contribute to a display that expresses care for the classroom environment in positive ways: for example, *We put things away, We mop up spills*, and so on. From time to time you could remind the children of what they have drawn and written. Establish the importance of doing things without being asked and emphasise that very often when something is neglected it is because we all think someone else will do it.

> **Vocabulary:** *care, look after, tidy, untidy.*

Right and wrong (page 28) is about knowing the difference between right and wrong. The children are asked to identify 'right' and 'wrong' actions. When discussing what makes some actions right or wrong, you could focus on the effects of these actions on other people. Also ensure the children understand that people's actions can have good and bad effects on people's property, on places and on animals. Establish that the children's behaviour should be based on their knowledge of what is right and what is wrong and not only in response to praise, rewards or punishments. Explore with the children why these things are right or wrong. Some children might be able to talk about why it is sometimes difficult to do what is right: for example, fear, temptation, and so on. The children could work in groups reading interactive electronic books in which they can talk about what a character can do and what is the right thing to do. An example would be one of the Choose and Tell: Nursery Rhymes from Inclusive Learning's Early Years Collection (see www.inclusive.co.uk/catalog/choosetell.shtml).

> **Vocabulary:** *bad, caring, effect, good, kind, mean, nasty, right, sorry, unkind, wrong.*

Our 'Do' rules and **Our 'Don't' rules** (pages 29–30) develop the children's awareness of boundaries which are set. They introduce the need for rules and can be linked with work on **Right and wrong**, page 28. This sheet can be used to help the children to contribute to a set of class rules which emphasise positive behaviour. Collect all their suggestions for rules and then help them to select the most important so that there are not too many to remember. During discussion or circle time, encourage the children to say why they chose a particular issue or why they should have that rule.

> **Vocabulary:** *because, do, don't, kind, mean, nasty, nice, share, snatch, take turns, unkind.*

Think ahead (page 31) is about the consequences of actions. It helps the children to recognise that their actions affect other people and to consider how. They develop an understanding of the need for rules and for thinking about others. The children could enact and then draw the consequences of the actions shown on the activity sheet. Higher-attaining children might be able to make up a longer story about the consequences of a wrong action.

> **Vocabulary:** *affect, because, cause, effect, so, then.*

Being kind and **Kindness badges** (pages 32–33) develop the children's ability and willingness to show care and concern for others. They focus on the kind actions people can do. Discuss how the children feel when someone is kind  to them. How is this different from when people do not bother or when they are unkind? The game can be linked with work in numeracy (Extend number recognition beyond 10; Begin to use ordinal numbers in different contexts).

> **Vocabulary:** *care, feelings, friend, give, help, hug, kind, nice, pleasant, share, unkind.*

Danger: 1 and **2** (pages 34–35) focus on the consequences of actions and on the children's developing ability to take appropriate responsibility for their own safety and well-being. As a homework activity they could talk to a parent, carer or other member of their family about anything at home that could be dangerous if not used properly or used by the wrong people and list five of them. Help them to categorise the dangers according to the headings *hot, sharp, poisonous* and *electric*. Discuss what might happen if they touch some of these items (you could provide home safety leaflets and read appropriate sections of them with the children). Encourage them to use sentences with *because* in them. A useful website is RoSPA (Royal Society for the Prevention of Accidents): www.rospa.co.uk.

> **Vocabulary:** *because, care, danger, effect, electric, hot, poison, poisonous, safe, sharp.*

Stop, Look, Listen (page 36) focuses on the consequences of actions and on the children's developing ability to take appropriate responsibility for their own safety and well-being. It reinforces the message of the Green Cross Code for road safety:

> First find a safe place to cross, then stop.
> Stop just before you get to the kerb.
> Look all around for traffic and listen.
> If traffic is coming, let it pass.
> When it is safe walk straight across the road – do not run.

To practise safe crossing, take the children into the playground or hall and practise crossing a 'road' chalked on the ground with 'pelican crossings'; these could be made from card shapes fixed to suitable pieces of games equipment (borrowed from Key Stage 2, if necessary). Use the Green Cross Code. Discuss what is meant by 'a safe place to cross' (a pelican crossing; with a crossing patrol; away from parked cars, trucks, and so on; away from bends and junctions). Higher-attaining children might be able to write simple instructions for crossing a road. A useful website with activities for children is www.roadsafetyuk.co.uk. See also the BBC's Tweenies website for an interactive activity on road safety:

www.bbc.co.uk/cbeebies/tweenies/storytime/stories/sirdoodles/index.shtml.

> **Vocabulary:** *across, cross, kerb, listen, look, pass, road, safe, safety, stop, straight, traffic, walk.*

Independence

The activities in this section develop the children's growing sense of responsibility for their own well-being and safety and for the safety and well-being of others. They include activities for developing self-regard, for taking pride in their achievements and for setting targets.

Wash your hands (page 37) is concerned with developing the children's ability to manage their own personal hygiene. Show the children your hands after handling something that will not make them obviously dirty but could leave micro-organisms on them: for example, an animal. Ask the children if your hands are clean. Explain that sometimes hands and objects such as cups or spoons can look clean but might have germs on them. Do the children know what germs are? Explain that they are tiny living things which can be seen only through a powerful microscope and which can make people ill. Show them a microscope and explain what it does. They could look at objects through a microscope but school microscopes are unlikely to be powerful enough to show micro-organisms. You could also show them magnified photographs of micro-organisms but emphasise that the pictures make them look much bigger than they really are. This page is connected with objectives in *Physical development* (Show awareness of healthy practices).

Health and safety: The children could make signs for the classroom to display in places where they might need to be reminded to wash their hands: for example, close to toilets, the canteen and where animals are housed. Signs could also be displayed during activities such as preparing food, planting seeds or bulbs or observing animals.

> **Vocabulary:** *clean, dirty, germ, ill, infection, soap, wash.*

My plan: 1 and **2** (pages 38–39) reinforce the children's learning from everyday school activities in which they take part and in which they have some choice. When they have set their tasks for the session, they can glue the pictures from page 38 (and/or other pictures they draw, as appropriate) onto the planning board on page 39.

Health and safety: Encourage the children to consider anything with which they might need to take special care: for example, using tools.

> **Vocabulary:** *do, first, follow, next, plan, task, then.*

Who can help? (page 40) focuses on developing the children's willingness to tackle problems and the need to ask others for guidance and support as they do so. Establish that everyone needs help at some time and that it is useful to know whom to ask for different types of help according to the nature of the task or problem in question. The children could begin by talking about the ways in which they help one another at school: for example, tying shoelaces, fastening aprons used for messy tasks, or carrying awkward or heavy things.

> **Vocabulary:** *ask, help, need, problem, task, who.*

I can do this (page 41) encourages the children to have pride in their achievements; it can also be used to help them to set realistic and achievable targets connected with their future learning. It can be linked with whole-class celebration of the achievements of  individuals, groups and the whole class, and can be used to encourage the children to share the pleasure of one another's achievements. They could bring in any awards or certificates they have received to show to the class and talk about.

> **Vocabulary:** *award, can, cannot, certificate, learn, plan, target.*

 Tidy time (page 42) can be used to reinforce the children's developing ability to use resources independently and to take initiatives in caring for their immediate environment. After playing the game, discuss why each action described on the game board is necessary in the classroom. How does it affect the room? What would it be like if no one did any of these actions? The BBC's Teletubbies website provides a tidying-up activity ('Noo-noo Tidies Up') in its Fun and Games section: www.bbc.co.uk/cbeebies/teletubbies/funandgames/.

> **Vocabulary:** *accident, clean, danger, messy, responsible, tidy, untidy.*

Fairness

In these activities the children learn what it means to be fair; also that sometimes when they say something isn't fair what they really mean is that they do not like it although it might be fair. They develop skills in co-operating with one another and learn how being fair helps to create a pleasant atmosphere in which everyone can play and learn.

Remind the children of **Fair play** (page 43) when they have difficulties in sharing classroom equipment. Is there anything which many of them want at the same time? Do the same children always seem to get what they want? Discuss what can be done about it. The children could use sand timers to limit the time they use something. Let them decide whether the timer allows them long enough or whether they should use a longer timer or set it more than once.

> **Vocabulary:** *fair, share, turns, unfair.*

Fair's fair (page 44) helps the children to show confidence and the ability to stand up for their rights by developing their sense of what is fair and unfair. Ask the children what they can see happening in the picture. With which children in the picture would they like to play? Why? With which ones would they not like to play? Why? After they have completed the activity, ask them to explain what makes some of the actions fair and some unfair. Draw out how both types of action affect the feelings of others. An online story on fairness can be found on the BBC's

Tweenies website: www.bbc.co.uk/cbeebies/tweenies/storytime/stories/itsnotfair/.

> **Vocabulary:** *fair, kind, mean, share, unfair, unkind.*

Fair deal (page 45) is about the times when the children say something isn't fair when they mean that they do not like it or they do not want to do something. The pictures are intended for use with a group of children, to stimulate discussion.

> **Vocabulary:** *fair, unfair.*

Awareness of places, cultures and needs

The activities in this section focus on the children's developing awareness and interest in cultural and religious differences. They also help to develop children's respect for people with different needs from their own.

My groups (page 46) is about the main group to which the children belong and the central place for that group (their family and home). It can be linked with **Stars**, page 14 and **Where I belong**, page 15. The topic could be introduced by reading *So Much!* by Trish Cooke (Candlewick Press), a story about a very big family and how members of the family get on together. How do they show love for one another? How do they help one another? Ask the children to count the family members. They could also count the people in their own families, to link with work in *Mathematical development*. What do people in the family in the book do? Invite them to compare this with what they do with their own families. Sensitivity to the circumstances of individual children in the class is advisable; some of the children may not live with their mother or father.

> **Vocabulary:** *baby, brother, carer, dad, family, father, gran, grandad, grandfather, grandmother, mother, mum, share, sister.*

A special gift (page 47) introduces the consideration of religious and cultural differences through the children's understanding of their own culture. You could read a story about gifts: for example, *The Sleeping Beauty*. What special gifts did the good fairies give to the princess? Could these presents be wrapped up? What presents would the children have given? The children could research and compare gifts given and received as part of religious festivals: for example, Christmas presents or gifts given to celebrate Divali. The activity can be linked to work in RE on celebrations.

> **Vocabulary:** *gift, give, present, wrap.*

Special days (page 48) focuses on religious and cultural differences through greetings cards. You could begin by providing a collection of greetings cards and asking the children to choose cards for specific people and occasions. How did they identify the occasions for which the cards were intended? Link this with literacy (Use cues  such as pictures to help with reading). It can also be linked to work in RE on celebrations. Explain to the children that every religion has its own special days: Christianity celebrates the birth of Jesus at Christmas; in India the end of the monsoon season is celebrated at Divali, a Hindu festival of lights associated with Rama and Sita and the goddess Lakshmi; Hanukkah is celebrated by Jews in December, when candles on a candelabrum are lit from the central candle for eight successive nights. Help the children to read the words on the cards. Which of these occasions do they celebrate? Do they know anyone who celebrates the others? They could also name other special days which people celebrate. Mark any forthcoming celebrations on a calendar. The BBC website provides an interactive page on which the children can design and send cards ('Post a Card with Puzzlesnuff'): www.bbc.co.uk/schools/laac/gallery/postcards/post.shtml.

> **Vocabulary:** *card, celebrate, gift, give, greetings, present, special, wishes.*

My special day (page 49) draws on the children's experiences of celebration – the ways in which celebration days are special and different from ordinary days: for example, people wear their best or special clothes, eat special foods, decorate their homes, visit people,  exchange gifts and cards, visit a place of worship and take part in special activities such as processions, games and parties. This is an opportunity to celebrate and show respect for the children's different cultural backgrounds and to encourage their interest in different cultures.

> **Vocabulary:** *card, decoration, game, gift, party, procession, special, worship.*

My special things (page 50) develops the children's awareness of cultural differences through exploring the special possessions of people from different backgrounds. Begin by showing the children a special possession of your own. Handle it with care and display it in a careful way to emphasise that it is precious. Explain why it is special and invite the children to ask questions about it. They could then talk to a partner about a special possession they have brought in and ask one another about these items. If there is little variation of culture within the class, invite someone from a different cultural background to come and show the children something special that they have which is closely connected to their culture. See the BBC's Teletubbies website for an interactive activity on special things ('Find the Favourite Things'): www.bbc.co.uk/cbeebies/teletubbies/funandgames.

> **Vocabulary:** *culture, special.*

My country and **An African country** (pages 51–52) develop awareness of cultures and places through exploring the children's knowledge of their own country. Link this work with geography. The children could find their own country on a map of the world and name and locate other countries they know: for example, places where they have had holidays. Show them some fruits (or pictures of fruits) and pictures of animals from their own country. If possible, read them *Handa's Surprise* by Eileen Browne (Walker Books), a story about a little girl who lives in Kenya in Africa. Help them to locate Africa and then Kenya on a map and to compare its position in the world with that of their own country. Ask the children if they can remember the names of the fruits that Handa carries in her

basket. What do they notice about the way in which Handa carries the basket of fruit? Do they ever carry things in this way? Explain that in many countries it is common for people to carry things on their head. The children could practise carrying safe items in a basket on their head. Ask them if they ever see any of the animals Handa meets. Do they ever see them in places other than zoos? Point out that these animals live in Kenya and some other hot countries but not in cooler countries, except in zoos. If *Handa's Surprise* is not available, you could help the children to research Kenya or another African country on the Internet or in information books before they complete page 52.

> **Vocabulary:** *Africa, country, gift, Kenya.*

Beautiful things (page 53) develops the children's awareness of the things around them and can be linked with work on *Knowledge and understanding of the world*. To prepare for the activity it is useful to collect pictures of beautiful things and places and even some objects of beauty. The children could bring in objects and pictures and talk about their ideas of what is beautiful. Include natural beauty such as volcanoes, raindrops on plants, frost-covered spiders' webs, close-ups of flowers, stones and animals.

> **Vocabulary:** *beautiful, beauty, colour, natural, nature, pattern, shape, shine, sparkle.*

Helen can't hear (page 54) develops the children's understanding that people have different needs. Help them to find out about the needs of people with hearing impairments from books such as *I Can't Hear Like You* by Althea (RNID/Dinosaur) or from organisations such as the Royal Association for Deaf people (www.royaldeaf.org.uk) and the Royal National Institute for Deaf People (www.rnid.org.uk). The children could learn the standard signs used for certain words, phrases and letters.

> **Vocabulary:** *deaf, ears, hard-of-hearing, hear, needs, sign, sign language.*

Sara can't speak (page 55) develops the children's understanding that people have different needs. Help them to find out about the needs of people who cannot speak from organisations such as the Royal Association for Deaf people (www.royaldeaf.org.uk) and the Royal National Institute for Deaf People (www.rnid.org.uk). The children could learn the standard signs used for certain words, phrases and letters.

> **Vocabulary:** *sign, sign language, speak, talk.*

Sunil can't see (page 56) develops the children's understanding that people have different needs. Help them to find out about the needs of people with sight impairments from organisations such as the Royal National Institute of the Blind (www.rnib.org.uk). They could find out about the various aids for people with limited vision, such as magnifiers and large-print books, as well as for people with no sight at all, such as canes, dogs and 'talking books'.

> **Vocabulary:** *blind, eyes, guide dog, needs, sight.*

William can't walk (page 57) develops the children's understanding that people have different needs. Help them to find out about the ways in which public buildings make access possible for wheelchair users: for example, by providing lifts or ramps and wide doorways. You could take them out to look at this type of provision locally. You could borrow a wheelchair for the children to try so that they can find out what it is like to use one; remind them that wheelchair users have to use one whenever they go out, although some of them might manage with walking aids for shorter distances.

Health and safety: A risk assessment should be carried out and school and LEA guidelines followed for any off-site visits.

> **Vocabulary:** *mobility, walk, wheelchair.*

Exploring

The activities in this section help to foster a willingness to explore and experiment within a safe environment. They encourage the children to ask questions, some of which might be difficult to answer, and to explore in order to develop knowledge and understanding. The activities help to develop the children's natural curiosity about the world around them and can be linked with work in *Knowledge and understanding of the world* (science and design technology).

I wonder where it goes (page 58) develops the children's natural curiosity about the events around them and helps them to learn about the services provided in the local community. You could show the children pictures of local refuse collection centres (tips, incinerators, and so on). Collect information from the local council and explain the process to the children using a flow chart. This could lead to work on recycling. Take the children to see a local recycling depot (or show them photographs of it). Which materials are recycled? Does the school recycle those materials?

> **Vocabulary:** *dustbin, recycle, rubbish, wastepaper basket, wheelie bin, where, wonder.*

I wonder where it begins (page 59) stimulates the children's curiosity by encouraging them to consider a difficult question and to suggest an explanation. This links with work in *Knowledge and understanding of the world* (science). Some children could look for information in books or on the Internet, but for others the explanations might be too difficult. The emphasis is on using the imagination to come up with an explanation.

> **Vocabulary:** *river, where, wonder.*

I wonder why we have money (page 60) develops the children's natural curiosity about the events around them and helps them to learn about the uses and sources of money.

Ask them if they have money of their own to spend. What do they spend it on, and where? Discuss other uses of money. What do their parents or carers use money for? Where do they get it from? This could be linked with work in maths on money.

> **Vocabulary:** *money, pence, pounds, spend, why, wonder.*

To prepare the children for **I wonder why people work** (page 61), discuss the reasons people need to work. Point out that adults work in order to earn money and that they need money to pay for food, a place to live, clothes and other items. Which pictures on this page show people working for money? You could introduce the term *wages*. Point out that many people cannot find work and so they can go to a post office to collect some money each week – enough to buy food and clothes and to pay for somewhere to live.

> **Vocabulary:** *earn, money, wages, why, wonder, work.*

What will happen? (page 62) stimulates the children's curiosity by encouraging them to consider a difficult question and to suggest an explanation. This question could be tested in work on *Knowledge and understanding of the world* (science), or they could look up the answer in books or on the Internet. For some children the explanations might be too difficult. The emphasis is on using the imagination to come up with explanations.

> **Vocabulary:** *bulb, flower, leaves, roots, water, what, why, wonder.*

All around (page 63) develops the children's curiosity and their exploratory impulse; it also encourages positive approaches to new experiences. It can be linked with exploring the environment of the classroom and school (indoors and outdoors). The children could draw what they think is really under each flap or use their imagination to think up something unusual and exciting. They will need help to cut out the flaps and to glue the sheet to another sheet without sticking the flaps down too.

> **Vocabulary:** *hidden, listen, look, what.*

What's inside? (page 64) develops the children's curiosity and their exploratory impulse; it also encourages positive approaches to new experiences. It can be linked with work in *Communication, language and literacy* (Use descriptive language).

> **Vocabulary:** *flat, hard, shiny, soft* (and other descriptive language).

We are good at this

- **Write what these animals are good at.**

I am good at

_____ .

a buzzing bee

I am good at

_____ .

a crowing cockerel

I am good at

_____ .

a swimming seal

I am good at

_____ .

a wriggling worm

Now try this!

- **Act out what you are good at.**
- **Write:** I am good at _____ .

Teachers' note Ask the children to name the animals. Help them to read the captions; emphasise the repeated sounds at the beginnings of the words. Ask them what each animal is good at but stress that there is no *right* answer: for example, a bee is also good at flying and finding bright flowers. The children could cut out or draw pictures of other animals and write captions modelled on these and then complete *I am good at …* sentences above.

Developing Citizenship
Year R
© A & C BLACK

12

Looking after Tom

- **Who can look after Tom?** ✔ or ✗

Pip ☐

Tom

Nan ☐

Dad ☐   Meg ☐

Now try this!

- **Find a photo of someone who looks after you.**
- **Glue it here.**
- **Write their name.**

```
┌ ─ ─ ─ ─ ─ ─ ─ ┐
│               │
│               │
│               │
│               │
│               │
│               │
└ ─ ─ ─ ─ ─ ─ ─ ┘
```

_____

Teachers' note Ask the children about the people who look after them at different times and in different places. Who looks after them most of the time? What does he or she do for them, and why? Who can look after them at school? How? Do their carers look after them differently now compared with when they were younger? If the children who tackle the extension activity cannot find a photo, they could draw one of their carers instead.

Developing Citizenship
Year R
© A & C BLACK

Stars

Who are your stars?

- **Draw them on the star shapes.**
- **Write captions.**

Anna is a star!

_____

is a star because ...

_____

_____

_____

_____

_____

is a star because ...

_____

_____

_____

_____

Now try this!

- **Tell a friend about your stars.**

Teachers' note Ask the children about the people who are special to them. Tell them that sometimes we call people who do special things _stars_. Who are the children's stars, and why? What do they do that makes them stars? Ask for examples. The children could draw pictures of their stars or glue on photographs of them before writing captions.

Developing Citizenship Year R
© A & C BLACK

Where I belong

- **Draw places where you belong.**
- **Draw yourself in the pictures.**

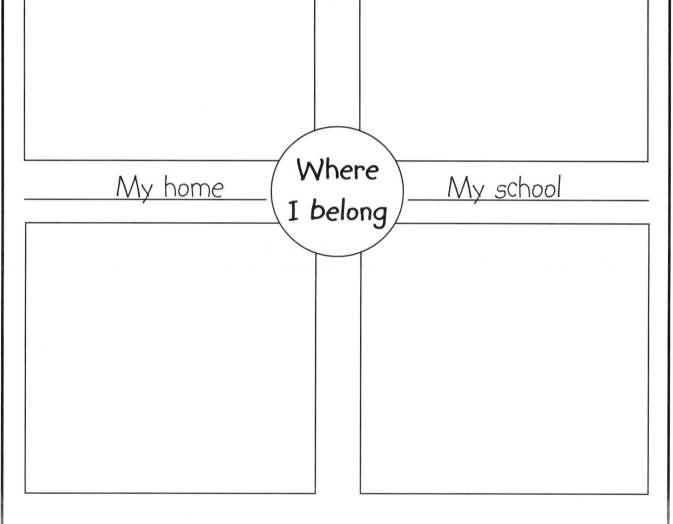

My home

Where I belong

My school

- **Write the names of these places.**

- **Write a list of the things you do in each place.**

Now try this!

Teachers' note Encourage the children to talk about their homes. What is special about them? Ask them to draw the part of their home they like best and to include themselves and other people in their drawing. Which part of the school do they like best, and why? Ask them to draw this place. Remind them that the school includes people. Invite the children to name other places to which they belong (see **Notes on the activities**, page 5).

Developing Citizenship
Year R
© A & C BLACK

Is it time?

• Tell the story.

• Draw what might happen next.

Teachers' note Ask the children about events they have looked forward to: for example, a birthday party, Christmas, Divali, a special day out. Do they ever ask their parents or carers if it is time yet? What do they say? How often do they ask? Invite them to tell the story in the pictures, or to act it in groups, and to say what is funny about it. Encourage the children to think about what might happen next.

Developing Citizenship Year R
© A & C BLACK

My big day

What is each child's big day?

- **Follow the strings.**
- **Write the names on the balloons.**

going to a football match

getting a bike

going on holiday

Divali

May

Ann

Raj

Ian

Now try this!

What was your big day?
- **Write what you enjoyed most.**

Teachers' note Invite the children to talk about a very special day. What did they do? Where? How did they feel before it? How did they feel on the day itself? Discuss the feelings they had after it was all over. Did they want to start again? On this page they should begin at the child's hand and follow the string, using a different coloured pencil for each line, until they reach the balloon, then write the correct name under the picture.

What I like

• **Cut out the picture cards. Sort them.**

I like	I do not like

beans

football

cats

snakes

apples

ice cream

rain

snow

bedtime

Now try this!

• **Make two more picture cards to add to each group.**

Teachers' note The cards could be cut out before the lesson or the children could do this for themselves. Ask them to glue them onto separate columns drawn on a sheet of paper, with the heading *I like* or *I do not like* glued at the head of each column.

Developing Citizenship
Year R
© A & C BLACK

Making friends

Eva makes a new friend.

- **Tell the story.**

How did you make a friend?

- **Draw your story.**

Now try this!

Teachers' note Enlarge this sheet and copy it onto an OHT. Mask all but the first picture and help the children to read the characters' names. What are Leo, Harry and Pilar doing? Why is Eva not playing? Encourage children around the class to share their ideas, which may differ. What do they think will happen? What else could happen? Discuss what they hope will happen before unmasking the other pictures. Encourage volunteers to tell the story.

Developing Citizenship
Year R
© A & C BLACK

Sam's pals

- **Make up friends for Sam.**

Word bank
ball   sit
TV   with

Sam likes to watch ____ with _____.

Sam likes to play ____ with _____.

Sam likes to ____ next to _____.

Sam likes to walk home ____ _____.

Now try this!

- **Write about something you like to do with a friend.**

I like to _____ with _____.

Teachers' note The children can make up names for Sam's friends; these could be names of their own friends if they choose. Read the incomplete sentences and invite volunteers to supply names for Sam's friends. Ask the children to use the word bank to fill the other blank spaces. What else might Sam do with his friends?

Developing Citizenship
Year R
© A & C BLACK

Tell me why

- ## Cut out the pictures.
- ## Make two stories.

- ## Tell a friend another story.

Teachers' note Ask the children about times when people who look after them tell them to do something. Do they always do as they are told? Do they sometimes say 'No'? If so, what happens? Do they sometimes ask 'Why?' What answers are they given? Help the children to cut out and sort the cards into two picture stories. They could then tell the stories to each other in pairs.

**Developing Citizenship
Year R**
© A & C BLACK

21

A time and a place

What can you do in the classroom? or

run ☒

shout ☐

write ☐

paint ☐

ride a bike ☐

read ☐

skip ☐

talk ☐

play ball ☐

Now try this!

• **Write two reasons why you can't play ball in the classroom.**

Teachers' note Ask the children to look at the pictures and to say what the children are doing. Point to the words and read them aloud. Why is there a cross in the box for *run*? Discuss why they should not run in the classroom. Where can they run? Draw out that it is acceptable to run in some places but not in others. They could discuss the pictures with a partner and decide on their answers together.

**Developing Citizenship
Year R**
© A & C BLACK

22

A helping hand

How do you help at home?

feeding a pet

tidying up

fetching things

playing with baby

listening

making your bed

cooking

shopping

cleaning

Now try this!

- **Draw something else you could do to help.**

Teachers' note Ask the children how the child in each picture is helping at home. Do they help in this way, too? If so, they should tick the box. Point out that they probably will not help in all of these ways. After the children have completed the sheet, encourage discussion about why it is good to help (see **Notes on the activities**, page 7).

Developing Citizenship
Year R
© **A & C BLACK**

A friend in need

• **Write what you would do for Lisa, Joe and Kat.**

Lisa

I would _____ .

| run away |
| tell a teacher |
| give her a hug |

Joe

I would _____ .

| help him |
| cry |
| ask what is wrong |

Kat

I would _____ .

| cry |
| help her |
| tell a teacher |

Now try this!

• **Tell a story about caring for a friend.**

Teachers' note Ask the children to look at the first picture and to describe how Lisa feels. How could a friend help her to feel happier? Discuss the different actions a friend could take and what they would do if their friend was crying: for example, ask what was the matter, listen and offer to help if they could; give her a hug; keep her company; invite her home. Use this model to discuss the other two pictures before the children complete the activity.

Developing Citizenship
Year R
© A & C BLACK

Pet care

What do they need?

Developing Citizenship
Year R
© A & C BLACK

Teachers' note Children who have pets could talk about what their pets need. Draw out that all animals need water and food and a safe place to shelter. Discuss the needs of animals kept at home or at school and establish that anyone who keeps an animal is responsible for meeting its needs. Ask the children to identify the animals and read the words in the thought bubbles before they use the word bank to write what each one needs.

Spick and span

1 START

2 You picked up rubbish. Go on 3.

3

4 You left bricks on the floor. Go back to START.

5

6

7 You swept up the sand. Go on 2.

8

9

10 You washed your paintbrush. Go on 3.

11 glue

12 You put the lid on the glue. Go on 1.

13

14 You left a book on the floor. Go back 1.

15 You didn't put the felt tip pens away. Go back 2.

16 You chewed a pencil. Go back 3.

17

18

19 You brought some flowers. Go on 3.

20

21

22

23 You dropped litter. Go back 2.

24 You wiped the table. Go on 3.

25

26

27

28 You mopped up water. Go to FINISH.

29 30 FINISH

You took care of the computer. Go on 3.

Teachers' note You need one copy of this page for a group of up to four children. They take turns to roll a die and move a counter the number of spaces indicated. Help them to read any words in the space on which they land. The winner is the first to finish. Afterwards, discuss why each action described on the game board matters. What would it be like if no one ever tidied up?

Developing Citizenship
Year R
© **A & C BLACK**

What a mess!

What should they do? Why?

• **Tell a friend.**

• **Draw what you can do to care for your classroom.**

• **Write a caption.**

Teachers' note You could cut out these pictures and ask the children to work in pairs; they talk about one of the pictures and decide what the children in the picture should do, and why. Invite them to share their ideas with the rest of the group.

Developing Citizenship
Year R
© A & C BLACK

Right and wrong

• **Write** right **or** wrong **in the boxes.**

• **Draw two more pictures:**

Doing right.   Doing wrong.

Teachers' note Invite the children to talk about what is happening in each picture and encourage them to try to read any words on the picture. Ask them to write 'right' on pictures which show someone doing the right thing and 'wrong' on those showing someone doing the wrong thing. Ask them to explain why each action is right or wrong. Reinforce why the second picture is 'right' even though the vase was broken.

**Developing Citizenship
Year R**
© **A & C BLACK**

28

Our 'Do' rules

- **What should you do?**
- **Make up rules.**

Your turn.

That's very good.

_____ _____

_____ _____

Now try this!

- **Tell a friend why you should keep to the rules.**

Teachers' note Tell the children that the children shown on this page have no rules in their classroom and that they are thinking some up. Invite them to describe what is happening in each picture and what is being done which is good. Model how to complete the first one: *Share things* or *Be kind* (or *nice*). Establish that rules should tell people what they should do as well as what they should not do.

Developing Citizenship
Year R
© A & C BLACK

Our 'Don't' rules

What should you not do?

• **Make up rules.**

Word bank

be
don't
hit
mean
nasty
snatch
unkind

Now try this!

• **Tell a friend why you should not do these things.**

Teachers' note It would be helpful if the children had first completed page 29. Ask them if they think everyone will follow a set of 'Do' rules. What other kind of rules are needed for anyone who does not? Ask them what is happening in each picture and to think up a rule telling the children what they should *not* do.

**Developing Citizenship
Year R
© A & C BLACK**

Think ahead

- ## Think what might happen next.
- ## Draw a picture.

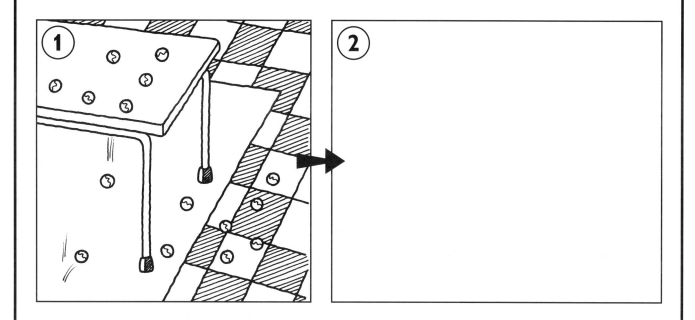

Teachers' note Discuss what is happening in each picture: someone has left marbles on a table top and someone has left a gate open. Encourage the children to describe what might happen because of these actions and ask them to draw pictures of the consequences. Some children could write a short sentence about one set of pictures.

Developing Citizenship
Year R
© A & C BLACK

Being kind

Four can play.

Teachers' note You need one copy of this page for a group of up to four children and four copies of page 33. The children take turns to roll a die and move a counter the number of spaces indicated. Help them to read any words in the space on which they land, ask them to say why those words mean being kind and give them a 'kindness badge'. At the end, reinforce the idea that everyone wins when we are kind to one another by giving everyone a 'Being a friend' badge.

Developing Citizenship Year R
© A & C BLACK

32

Kindness badges

Playing together

Hugging

Helping

Listening

Being a friend

Saying sorry

Caring

Sharing

Being a friend

Being a friend

Giving

Saying something nice

Teachers' note Use this with page 32. Glue the page onto A4 card before cutting out the badges. Ask the children to colour them in, then attach a safety pin to the back of each badge with sticky tape. After playing the game, discuss the effect of each action on the game board. How does it make someone feel? What would it be like if no one did these things? You could also use the 'kindness badges' as rewards for children who act kindly towards others.

Developing Citizenship Year R
© A & C BLACK

33

Danger: 1

Danger! We must not touch these things.

• **Sort the dangers into sets.**

hot

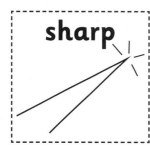
sharp

poisonous

electric

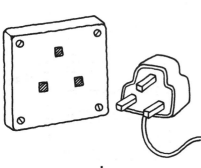
socket

fire

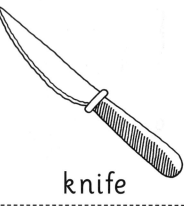
knife

scissors

pan

kettle

hairdryer

bleach

foxglove

Teachers' note Use this with page 35. Use these pages to introduce to the children the idea of taking responsibility for their own safety. Ask them to name some items that could harm them at home. Write up their responses in columns according to the type of danger (hot, sharp, poisonous or electric). They could look for other hot, sharp, poisonous or electric items at home and list or draw five of them for homework.

Developing Citizenship
Year R
© A & C BLACK

Danger: 2

tablets

light

tools

pins

medicine

oven

lamp

polish

stapler

heater

fan

tin

Teachers' note Use this with page 34. The picture cards could be cut out before the lesson or the children could cut them out for themselves before sorting them according to the headings.

Developing Citizenship
Year R
© A & C BLACK

35

Stop, Look, Listen

- **Put the pictures in order.**
- **Read the words.**
- **Tell a friend the right way to cross a road.**

Cross the road

Stop

Listen

Look

Now try this!

- **Tell a friend what you should do while you are crossing the road.**

Teachers' note The children first need to be shown the Green Cross Code (see **Notes on the activities**, page 8). Emphasise the words *Stop*, *Look* and *Listen* and ask the children where they should stop, what they should look and listen for and then what they should do. Make clear that they should continue looking and listening as they cross a road.

Developing Citizenship Year R © A & C BLACK

Wash your hands

When should you wash your hands?

- **Write** before **or** after .

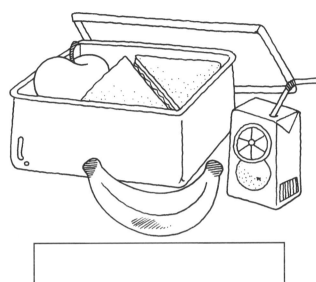

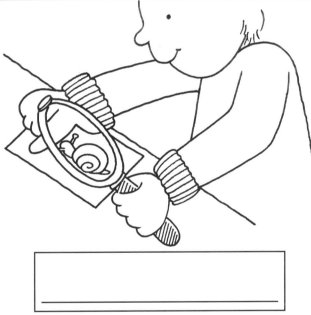

- **Copy the sentence and fill in the gaps.**

We wash our hands after _____

because _____ .

Teachers' note This could be used to assess the children's level of understanding about personal hygiene. Discuss the best way to wash hands – with warm water and soap, and stress the importance of drying them properly. Point out that we need to wash our hands before some activities (for example, cooking or eating) and after others (for example, handling animals or soil or going to the toilet). Introduce the idea of germs (see **Notes on the activities**, page 8).

Developing Citizenship
Year R
© A & C BLACK

My plan: 1

Plan what you are going to do.

- **Draw three more activities. Write captions.**
- **Cut out the pictures.**

 read	 write	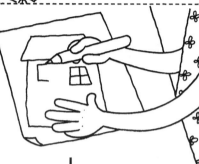 draw
 paint	 model	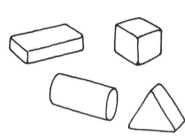 build
 make music	 dress up	 do a puzzle

Teachers' note This can be used with page 39. The blank cards can be filled in with appropriate activities, depending upon what the children can do at school. At the beginning of a suitable session, explain to the children what they are expected to do during the session and what choices they have. Help them to make their choices and to represent them using picture cards.

Developing Citizenship
Year R
© A & C BLACK

My plan: 2

Make your plan.

- **Glue the pictures here.**
- **Write the words.**

First I shall _____

_____

_____

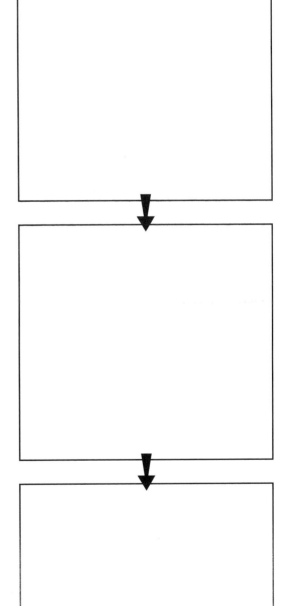

Next I shall _____

_____

_____

Then I shall _____

_____

_____

Teachers' note Use this with page 38. Once the children have made their choice of activities, discuss which they will do first. They should glue the picture card in the first box and say 'First I shall … '. Repeat this for their second and third activities, using the words *Next* and *Then* in place of *First*. During the session, remind the children of their plan when they move from one activity to another. This type of planning could become part of the daily routine.

Developing Citizenship
Year R
© **A & C BLACK**

Who can help?

Who can help you ...

Write their names.

... to make a model?

_____

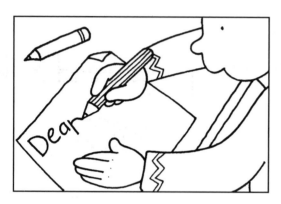

... to write a letter?

_____

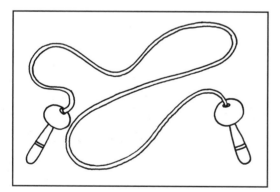

... to learn to skip?

_____

Now try this!

Who else can help you?

How can they help?

• **Tell a friend.**

Teachers' note Ask the children about the activities with which they need help. You could discuss times when they have been helped but didn't want help – preferring to do it by themselves. Also ask them about the help they can give other children and adults. Draw out that everyone needs help at some time. Ask the children what they used to need help with but can now do on their own.

Developing Citizenship
Year R
© **A & C BLACK**

I can do this

• **Tick what you can do.**

write
my name ☐

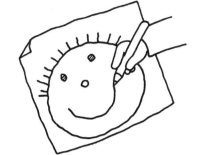

draw
a face ☐

do up
buttons ☐

ride
a bike ☐

score
a goal ☐

swim ☐

make
music ☐

cut out
shapes ☐

use a
mouse ☐

Now try this!

• **Draw something you would like to learn to do.**

• **Write a caption.**

Teachers' note Help the children to read the instruction and to identify the activities represented on the picture cards, which should not be cut out until the children have ticked the relevant ones; these can be glued onto a chart under the heading *I can do this*. The others can be used to help the children to set targets. What would they like to be able to do? They could practise it and then glue the card onto their chart once they can do the activity.

Developing Citizenship Year R
© A & C BLACK

41

Tidy time

Four can play.

Teachers' note You need one copy of this page for a group of up to four children. Play as for 'Snakes and ladders': take turns to roll a die and move a counter the number of spaces indicated. Help the children to read any words in the space on which they land. Before they move, ask them to explain why landing on a space with the word 'Tidy' is rewarded by going up a ladder and landing on a space with the word 'Untidy' involves sliding down a snake.

**Developing Citizenship
Year R**
© A & C BLACK

Fair play

What is wrong in this story?

- **Tell a friend.**

- **Change the story.**
- **Make it fair.**
- **Tell a friend your new story.**

Teachers' note Ask the children if the first picture is fair. They might think it is not fair that the girl has the tricycle but the boys don't. Point out that only one person at a time can use it. Is the second picture fair? Point out that it depends how long the girl has been on the tricycle. If she has been using it for a long time is the third picture fair? What should the boys have done?

Developing Citizenship
Year R
© **A & C BLACK**

43

Fair's fair

Is this fair?

• **Write** **yes** **or** **no** .

• **Draw the picture again so that everything is fair.**

Now try this!

Teachers' note Ask the children to describe what is happening in the picture. Can they spot anything which is not fair? They should write 'yes' or 'no' in the boxes beside each pair of children to show whether what they are doing is fair or not. Afterwards invite them to share their responses and to say why each action is fair or unfair.

Developing Citizenship
Year R
© A & C BLACK

Fair deal

Is it fair? Why?

- **Talk to a partner.**

- **Draw something that you once said was not fair.**

Teachers' note Ask the children if each picture is fair. They might say no because each one shows a child saying 'It's not fair'. After they have discussed the pictures with a partner, ask them whether each one really is unfair. Why are the children in the pictures saying it isn't fair? What do they really mean? (They do not want to do as they are told.)

Developing Citizenship
Year R
© A & C BLACK

My groups

• **Draw and label some of the people in your home.**

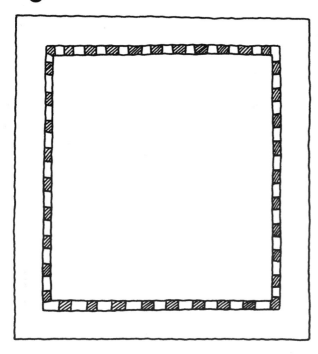

Now try this!

• **Draw another group you belong to.**

• **Write labels.**

Teachers' note Discuss the meaning of 'family': that it can mean mothers, fathers, brothers, sisters, and so on (even if they live in different places) but that it can also be used for people who share a home. For the extension activity, encourage the children to think about other groups they belong to: for example, the children they sit with at school or a group of friends or cousins they play with at home.

**Developing Citizenship
Year R**
© A & C BLACK

A special gift

- **Draw the present in the parcel.**
- **Write on the tag.**

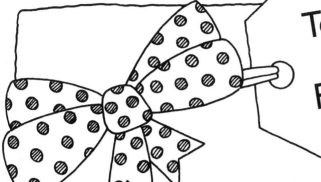

To

From

- **Write about the present.**

Now try this!

Teachers' note Ask the children about a present they have given to someone (introduce the word *gift* for present). How did they choose it? They could talk about what they knew about the person the gift was for and how they knew what he or she would like. Ask them to decide who this present is for and what they would like to give to him or her. Afterwards invite them to talk about why they chose it.

Developing Citizenship
Year R
© **A & C BLACK**

Special days

• **Match the cards to the special days.**

Christmas

birthday

Hanukkah

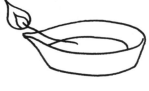

Divali

• **Make a card for another special day.**

Teachers' note Link this to work in RE on celebrations. With the children, read the words on the cards and the names of the special days. Which of these do they celebrate? (See **Notes on the activities**, pages 9–10.) Ask them to draw lines to link the cards to the pictures.

Developing Citizenship
Year R
© A & C BLACK

My special day

My special day was _____.

- **Draw what you wore, what you ate and what you did.**

My special clothes	My special food

Special things I did

Which special people were there?

- **Write their names.**

Teachers' note Ask the children about a celebration day they remember. What were they celebrating? Discuss how celebration days are different from ordinary days. How do they feel on a special day and what special things do they do? Read the headings and ask the children how their clothes, food and what they do are different on special days. Ask them to draw their special clothes, food and activities. Some children could label their pictures.

Developing Citizenship
Year R
© A & C BLACK

My special things

- **Draw one of your special things.**
- **Write some labels.**

- **Tell a friend about another of your special things.**

Teachers' note Begin with your own and the children's special possessions (see **Notes on the activities**, page 10). Ask them to draw something special in the frame and then to write labels to show what is special about it: for example, colour, pattern, important parts of it, and so on.

Developing Citizenship
Year R
© A & C BLACK

My country

My country is

- **Draw and colour its flag.**

These fruits grow here.

These animals live here.

- **Draw and write something else about your country.**

Now try this!

Teachers' note Link this with geography (see **Notes on the activities**, page 10). Point out that different countries have different plants and animals because they have hotter, colder, wetter or drier weather. The children could talk about different plants and animals they have seen on holiday abroad. Ask them to think of fruit they have seen growing in their own country. What animals have they seen here?

Developing Citizenship
Year R
© A & C BLACK

An African country

The African country is

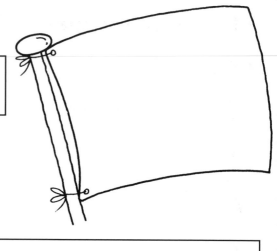

• **Draw and colour its flag.**

These fruits grow there.

These animals live there.

• **Write three words about this African country.**

Teachers' note It would be helpful if the children had read *Handa's Surprise* by Eileen Browne (see **Notes on the activities**, page 10). Tell them that Handa lives in Kenya (show them its location on a map). What can they find out from the book (or from other sources such as the Internet) about Kenya or another African country? What fruits grow there? What animals live there? How is it different from their country?

Developing Citizenship
Year R
© A & C BLACK

Beautiful things

- **Cut out pictures of beautiful things.**
- **Glue them here.**

A beautiful place

A beautiful flower

A beautiful bird

A beautiful animal

Now try this!

- **Draw another beautiful thing.**
- **Write a caption.**

Teachers' note Let the children look through pictures in books and magazines. Discuss which ones they think are beautiful and what they like about them. Provide magazines from which they can cut pictures to glue into the appropriate frames on this page.

Developing Citizenship
Year R
© A & C BLACK

Helen can't hear

Helen can't hear.

What can she do?

Word bank
feel
play
smell
taste

Helen can _____

Helen can _____

Helen _____

_____

Now try this!

How could you talk to Helen?

- **Tell the other children in your class.**

Teachers' note Different groups could work on this page and on pages 55–57. They first need to have done some preparation work on what it means to have a hearing impairment. They could experience this by wearing earmuffs designed to keep out sounds and discussing what difference it makes not to be able to hear. Establish that we can all do certain things better than others and that Helen can do other things well.

Developing Citizenship
Year R
© A & C BLACK

Sara can't speak

Sara can't speak.
What can she do?

Sara can _____

Sara can _____

Sara _____

_____

Now try this!

How can Sara talk to her friends?
• **Tell the other children in your class.**

Teachers' note Different groups could work on this page, on page 54 and on pages 56–57. They first need to have done some preparation work on the problems faced by people who cannot talk or have a speech impairment and how they can overcome them (see **Notes on the activities**, page 10). Stress that we can all do certain things better than others and that Sara can do other things well.

Developing Citizenship
Year R
© A & C BLACK

Sunil can't see

Sunil can't see.

What can he do?

Sunil can _____

Sunil can _____

Sunil _____

How can Sunil find his way around?

• **Tell the other children in your class.**

Now try this!

Teachers' note Different groups could work on this page, on pages 54–55 and on page 57. They first need to have done some preparation work on what it means to have a sight impairment. They could experience this by wearing a blindfold and having a friend guide them across a mat (see **Notes on the activities**, page 10). Make clear that we can all do certain things better than others and that Sunil can do other things well.

Developing Citizenship
Year R
© **A & C BLACK**

William can't walk.

What can he do?

Word bank
catch
sing
talk
write

Here we go, here we go …

William can _____

William can _____

William _____

Now try this!

How can William play sport?
• Tell the other children in your class.

Teachers' note Different groups could work on this page and on pages 54–56. They first need to have done some preparation work on the reasons why some people cannot walk or can walk only a little (see **Notes on the activities**, page 11). Emphasise that we can all do certain things better than others and that William can do other things well.

Developing Citizenship
Year R
© A & C BLACK

I wonder where it goes

Where does the rubbish go?

- **Cut out the pictures.**
- **Put them in order.**

Now try this!

Where do you think it goes next?

- **Draw the last picture.**

Teachers' note The children should be able to put the pictures in order to show what happens to rubbish from the classroom bin, but do they know where the refuse truck takes it? (See **Notes on the activities**, page 11.)

Developing Citizenship
Year R
© A & C BLACK

I wonder where it begins

I wonder where the river begins.

What do you wonder?

- **Draw a picture and complete the sentence.**

I wonder where _____

_____

What do you think is the answer?

- **Write about your ideas.**

Now try this!

Teachers' note Begin with an 'I wonder where…' statement such as 'I wonder where the moon goes in the daytime.' Wait for the children to respond; once one child has made a suggestion, encourage the others to join in the conversation by asking them if they think the suggestion is right, and why – or why not. Emphasise that they are not expected to know the answers but to think up their own ideas.

Developing Citizenship
Year R
© A & C BLACK

I wonder why we have money

I wonder why we have money.

Who needs money?

- **Colour them.**

What would it be like without money?

Now try this!

- **Tell a friend.**

Teachers' note Ask the children to look for people in the pictures who need money. What do they need it for? Draw out that we give money in exchange for many things: for example, petrol, phone calls, sweets and other goods from shops. Discuss how their parents or carers pay for things they buy in supermarkets. They might not give coins or banknotes but use a plastic card instead. Point out that this means that the money is taken from their bank and given to the shop.

Developing Citizenship
Year R
© A & C BLACK

I wonder why people work

Who is working? ☑

Why do people work?
• Tell a friend about your ideas.

Teachers' note Ask the children to name some kinds of work they do. What kinds of work do people in their families do? (Include work in the home such as looking after a baby, housework and decorating.) After the children have completed the activity, invite them to compare their answers. Point out any differences and discuss how they decided if activities were work. The children might find it difficult to come to any conclusions, but help them to distinguish between play and work.

Developing Citizenship
Year R
© A & C BLACK

What will happen?

What do you think will happen to the bulb?

- **Draw and label your ideas.**

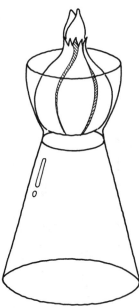

- **Write two sentences.**

Word bank

bulb
flower
leaves
roots
water

What will happen here?

- **Write a sentence.**

Teachers' note The children could first look at some real-life wonders of nature, such as buds appearing on flowers or seeds sprouting. What makes these events happen? Show the children the picture and ask them what it is. What will happen to the bulb? They can draw their ideas on this page and label their drawings with the help of the word bank.

**Developing Citizenship
Year R**
© A & C BLACK

All around

- **Cut the flaps and glue the page onto another sheet.**
- **Draw a picture behind each flap.**

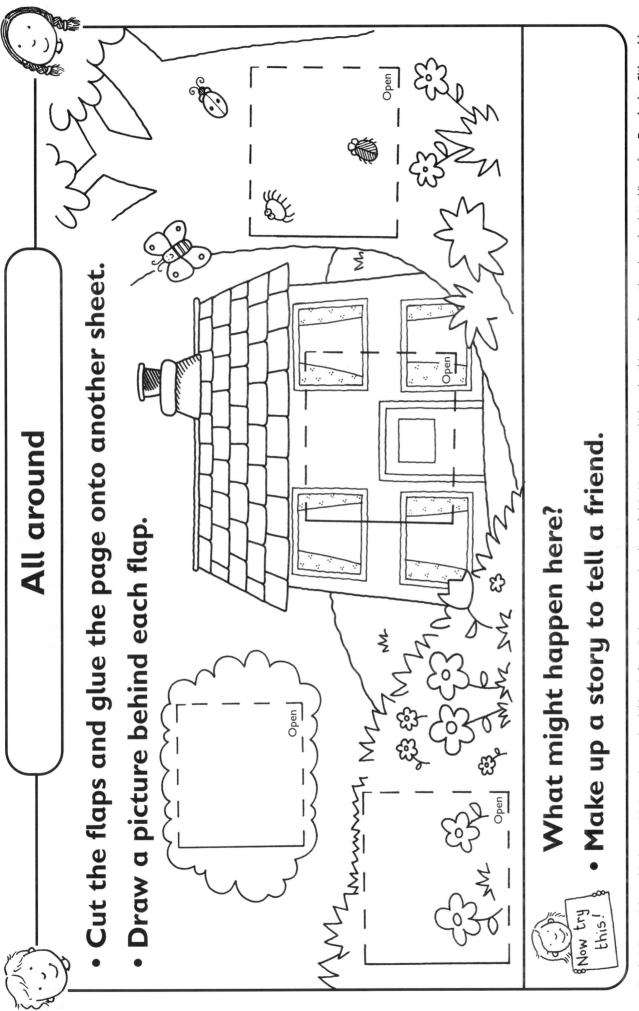

Open

Open

Open

Open

- **What might happen here?**
- **Make up a story to tell a friend.**

Now try this!

Teachers' note Enlarge this sheet to A3 size and group the children in fours. Each group needs a sheet of plain A3 paper on which to glue this page after cutting along the dotted lines of the flaps. These are easier to cut if they are folded across to the centre first. Once the children (with adult assistance if necessary) have cut the flaps, stuck the page down and folded the flaps back, they can draw one picture each. What would they like to find under each flap? What might be hiding or have been hidden there? They could display their sheets and make up a story about the objects they drew.

**Developing Citizenship
Year R
© A & C BLACK**

What's inside?

What's in the box?

It's flat.

- **Draw the object.**
- **Write one more clue.**

It's shiny.

It's hard.

- **Put something in a box.**
- **Give a friend clues.**

Now try this!

Teachers' note Show the children a 'mystery box' in which you have hidden something (for example, a glove, a piece of fruit or a ball). Describe the object, bit by bit, and ask them at each stage if they can guess what it is. Show them the contents of the box. Were they right? On this page the children should draw the mystery object described by the circus performers (for example, a coin, a credit card, a CD or DVD, a ruler, a mirror) and add a fourth clue in the blank speech bubble.

Developing Citizenship
Year R
© A & C BLACK